Home Po

C000039207

Compiled by John F

OXFORD

Oxford University Press, Walton Street, Oxford, OX2 6DP

Oxford New York Toronto
Delhi Bombay Calcutta Madras Karachi
Kuala Lumpur Singapore Hong Kong Tokyo
Nairobi Dar es Salaam Cape Town
Melbourne Auckland Madrid

and associated companies in
Berlin Ibadan

Oxford is a trade mark of Oxford University Press

© Oxford University Press 1994
ISBN 0 19 916686 2
Printed in Hong Kong

A CIP Catalogue record for this book is available from the British
Library

Acknowledgements
The Editor and Publisher wish to thank the following who have kindly
given their permission for the use of copyright material:

Tony Bradman for 'If you're a snail' © 1993 Tony Bradman; Sarah
Matthews for Stanley Cook's 'A tent' from *Come along again* © 1982
Stanley Cook; David Harmer for 'Where we live' © 1993 David
Harmer; Trevor Harvey for 'My home' © 1993 Trevor Harvey; Tony
Mitton for 'Castle', 'My den', 'High and dry' and 'Empty cottage' all ©
1993 Tony Mitton.

Although every effort has been made to contact the owners of
copyright material, a few have been impossible to trace, but if they
contact the Publisher, correct acknowledgement will be made in
future editions.

Illustrations by
Gini Wade   Caroline Crossland
Claire Pound   Rhian Nest James
Jenny Williams   Andrew Tewson
Ann Johns   Thelma Lambert

If you're a snail

If you're a snail
It's on your back;
If you're a mouse
It's in a haystack.

If you're a bird
It's up in a tree;
If you're a fish
It's deep in the sea.

2

If you're a lion
It's out on the plain;
If you're a rat
It's down the drain.

But if it's your home
That you're looking for,
It's that place with four walls
A roof and a door!

Tony Bradman

3

Castle

I wish I lived in a castle
with flags and pointed towers.
I'd stand up high on the battlements
and look at the land for hours.

And if I spotted a dragon
or a giant, looking bored,
I'd strap on all my armour
and chase it away with my sword.

Tony Mitton

My den

With a cardboard crate
and an empty sack,
a broken buggy
and a plastic mac,

down in my garden
under the tree,
I've built a home
and it's just for me.

Tony Mitton

A tent

The walls of a house
Are far too thick
For you to fold it
And take it away
On holiday.

But a tent is so thin
That you can pack
Its roof and walls
Into one small sack
And carry it on your back.

Stanley Cook

9

Where we live

Some of us live in a house made of bricks.

Some of us live in a house made of stone.

I live with my Mum and Dad, my Gran lives on her own.

Some of us live in a block
of high flats.

Some of us live in a small
bungalow.

Some of us live in a caravan,
some have nowhere to go.

David Harmer

High and dry

In swampy places
homes are found
that stand on stilts
above the ground.
The wooden stilts
are sunk in mud
to keep the homes
above the flood.

Tony Mitton

12

Empty cottage

Down at the end
of the country lane,
there's an empty cottage
with cracked window panes.

The door's off its hinges.
The roof tiles leak.
The only sounds
are a rustle and creak.

Only the spider,
the slug and the louse
live in the shell
of the old empty house.

Tony Mitton

My home

My home is a brick house
Where it's warm and safe to be;
I wish all the world's children
Could be lucky, like me.

Trevor Harvey